What I Know About Living Things

1. Draw, write, or do both, to show two things that you already know about living things.

   What I know:

2. What would you like to discover about living things? Write your question below.

   My question: _____
   _____
   _____

3. Why do you think it is important to learn about life on Earth and how it works?

   _____
   _____
   _____
   _____

Alive or Not Alive?

Sorting things into groups by what they do or how they look is called **classifying**.

1. Look at the diagrams of things. Classify and sort them into two groups: alive or not alive. Write each one in the correct column of the table.

Plant   Fish   Chair   Man

Stones   Window   Horse

Alive	Not alive

2. Name one more thing that you think is alive.

_____

3. Explain why you think it is alive.

_____

Science Skills

Looking for Living Things - Record it!

1. Write or draw what you found on your search for life around your school. Decide how to organise your work so that you can classify everything you have found into two groups: living and non-living.

2. What did you find that you were not sure how to classify?

   _____
   _____

3. Why was it difficult to decide?

   _____
   _____

Once Alive or Never Alive?

Non-living things may have never been alive or may have once been alive.

1 Name three things that have never been alive.

_____

2 Name three things that were once alive.

_____

3 Here are three chickens.

Hen   Cuddly chicken   Wooden chicken

a Which chicken has never been alive?

_____

b Which chicken was once alive?

_____

c Which chicken is alive?

_____

d How did you decide?

_____

Compare the Babies

Compare a doll and a human baby by thinking about what features they have and what they can do.

1   How is a baby doll like a human baby?

A baby can _____ and a doll can too.

2   How is a baby doll different from a human baby?

A baby can _____ but a doll cannot.

3   Draw a baby doll and label features that show it is not alive.

4   Write sentences about your drawing.

What can Living Things Do?

1 Find the living things in the diagram.

   _____

2 How do you know they are alive?

   _____

3 Tick the words that you think all living things do.

   stay the same ☐   use batteries ☐

   move ☐   have babies ☐

   burn ☐   grow ☐

   feed ☐   have senses ☐

Growing Up

As living things get older, they **grow** and change.

1. **Draw what you think these living things will look like when they have grown up. Label any features that have changed.**

Adult

A seedling (young plant)

Adult

A kitten

2. **Draw a young living thing of your choice, and its adult.**

Baby

Adult

How Have You Changed?

Human babies need to be looked after by **adults** as they cannot do much for themselves. They would not survive if they were not looked after.

1. **How have you changed since you were a baby? List three things you can do now that you could not do when you were a baby.**

   _____
   _____
   _____

2. **Draw yourself as a baby, as you are now, and then how you think you will look as an adult. Label your drawings to show the changes.**

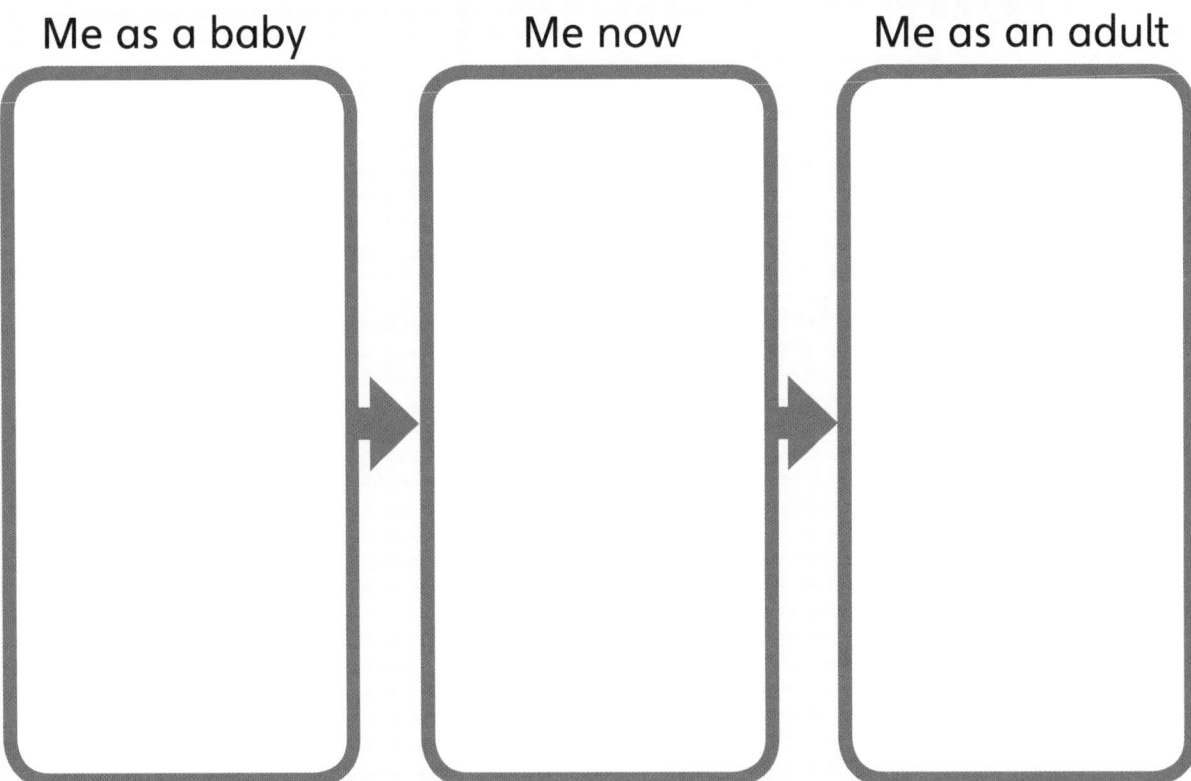

Me as a baby → Me now → Me as an adult

That's My Parent!

Living things often look like their **parents**. But sometimes the **offspring** (baby) has a different name from the parent.

1. Choose from the word list below and write the name of the offspring next to each parent in the table.

   frogspawn   foal   tomato seeds   kitten

Parent	Offspring (baby)
Cat	
Horse	
Frog	
Tomato plant	

2. Name each of the living things below by choosing a word from the list.

   palm tree   date   caterpillar   butterfly

3. Draw a line between each parent and its offspring. Add both parent and offspring to the table above.

Living Things

Some baby living things look **similar** to their parents and some look very different.

4   Choose one parent and offspring. Think about their size, shape, features (which is what we call important parts of something) and what they can do.

5   Make a poster in the space below to show what is similar and what is different.

Compare parent and offspring

6   What do you think would happen if living things stopped producing offspring?

The Circle of Life

The stages of life for a living thing are called its **lifecycle**.

1. These stages in the human lifecycle are mixed up. Put them in the correct order.

    older child   toddler   adult   baby   teenager

2. Write each one in the boxes on the lifecycle diagram below.

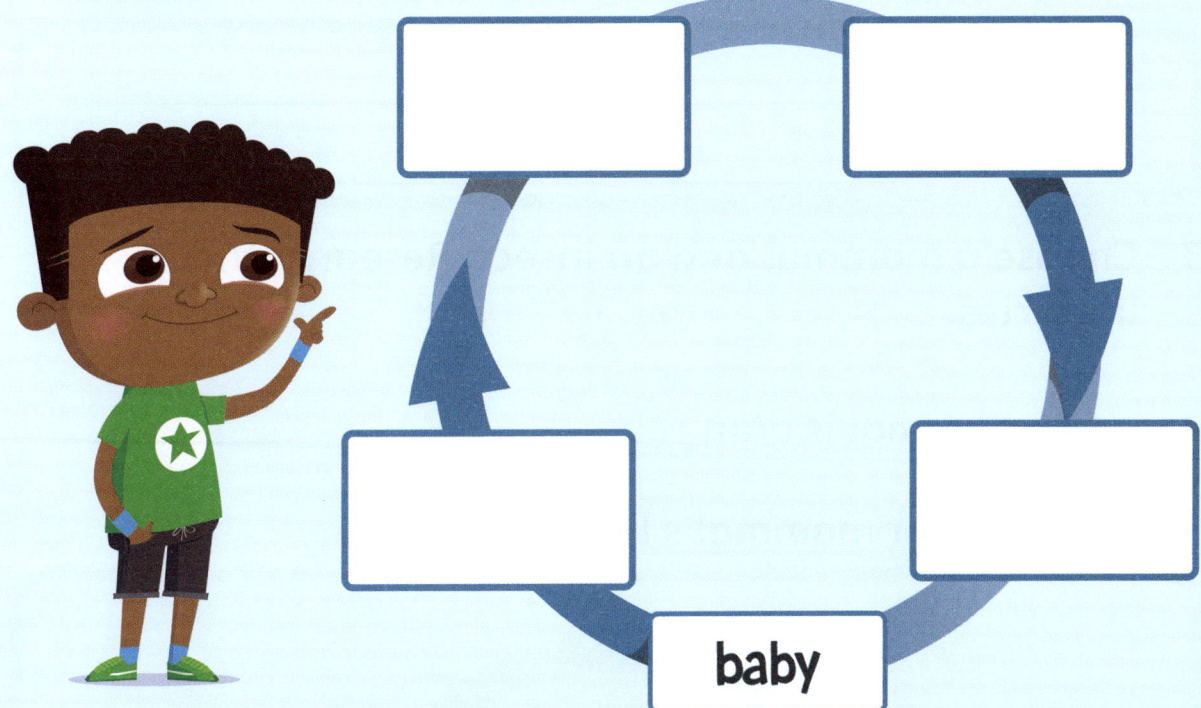

3. Why do you think a lifecycle is sometimes called the circle of life? Tick the correct answer.

    … because living things all spin and move around in circles. ☐

    … because the offspring of living things grow to be adults and have their own offspring so life carries on. ☐

Compare Animal Lifecycles

Lifecycles for different animals can be very different.

1. Name three animals that lay eggs.

2. Name three animals that give birth to live babies.

3. Choose a mammal and an insect. Research their lifecycles.

    a My mammal is a/an _____

    b Label your mammal's lifecycle.

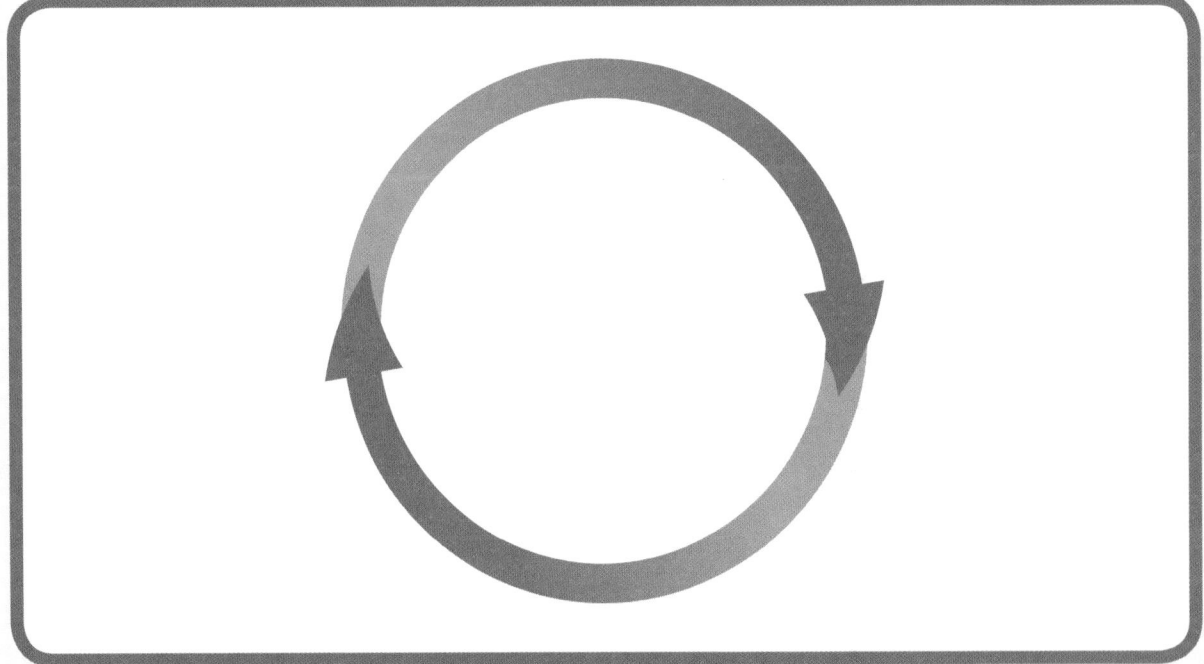

Living Things

c My insect is a/an _____

d Label your insect's lifecycle.

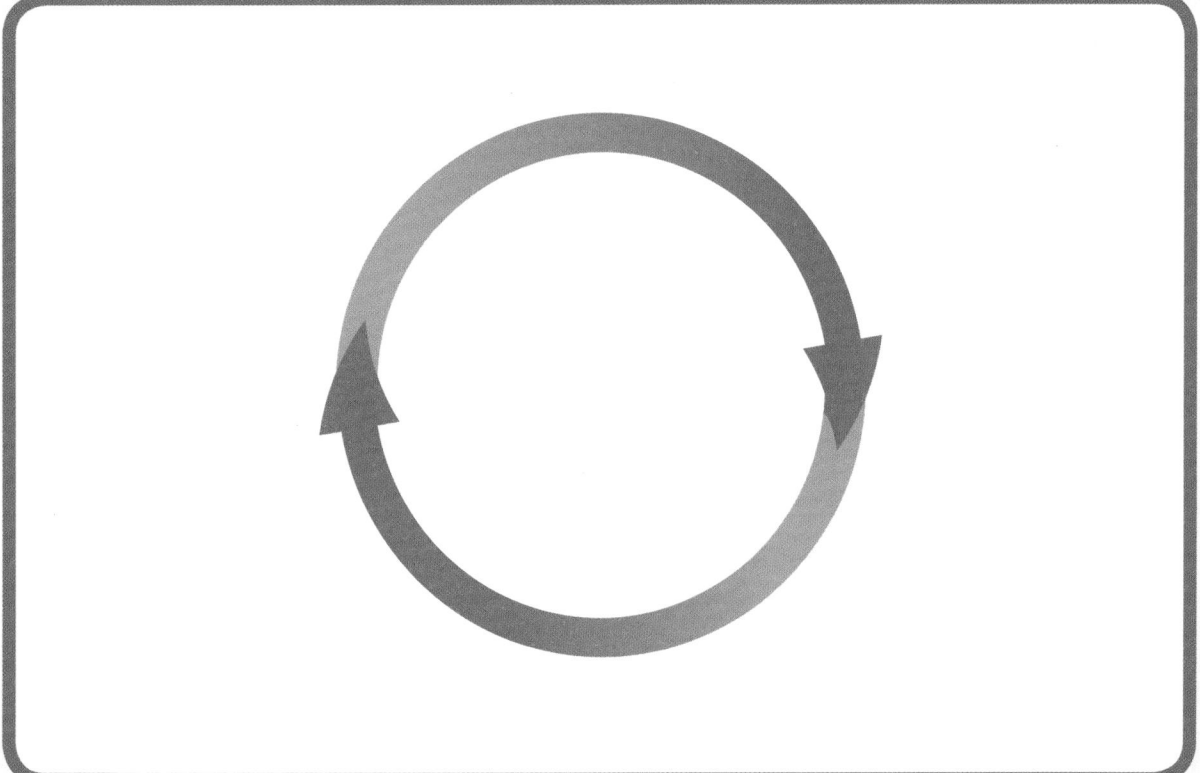

4 Complete the sentences using the words from a or b to compare the lifecycles of your mammal and insect.

a an adult lays eggs that hatch

b an adult gives birth to a live baby

My mammal's offspring is produced when

My insect's offspring is produced when

Match the Pairs!

Design a *Match the Pairs* game for three living things using the card shapes below. Include at least one plant and one animal.

For each living thing draw a parent on one shape and its baby on another. Make sure you don't put them next to each other!

Play with a partner. Can they point to the three pairs?

If you have time, draw your designs again on some cardboard shapes to make a real card game. You could add more living things or combine them with other pupils' cards. The more you have, the harder the game.

A Plant Lifecycle

Plants are living things so they grow up, produce baby plants, get older and in time, die.

1. Choose a plant you know and label its lifecycle.

   a My plant is _____

   b Label your plant's lifecycle

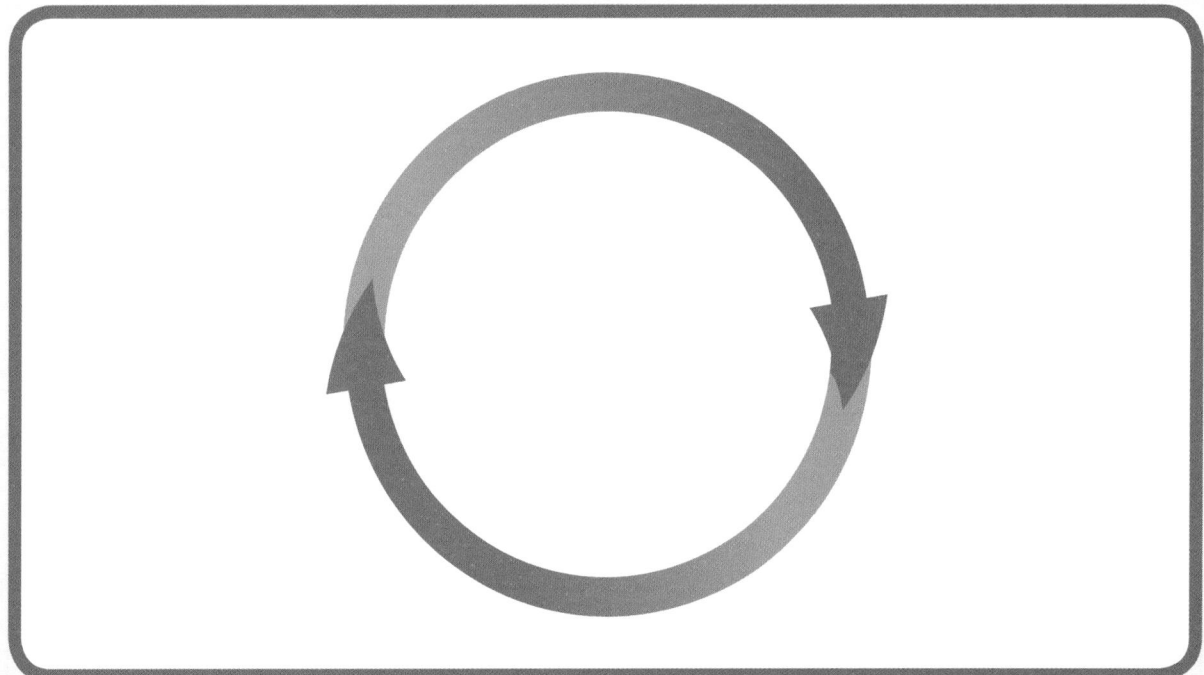

2. Complete this sentence:

My plant produces offspring called _____

3. What happens as the offspring of your plant grows?

What Have You Learned?

1. Show something you have learned about the topics in the boxes below. You could write a sentence, draw a picture or do both.

What all living things do	Non-living things
Classifying	**Lifecycles**

2. Look at your first page in this workbook when you started the topic of Living Things. Have you changed any of your ideas? What new things have you learned?

_____
_____
_____